RUBRICS AND CHECKLISTS 1-3

TABLE OF CONTENTS

RUBRICS

A rubric's purpose is twofold. First, a rubric is a tool used to assess a piece of work which a student has produced. Second, a rubric is a method of expressing the distinctions between the qualities of work.

Usually criteria are recorded in the left hand column and varying degrees of the quality of work is described in the columns to the right. A rubric clarifies what makes a good piece of work excellent and provides reference for next steps to improve work.

A successful rubric:

❖ helps teachers describe excellence.

❖ helps teachers plan how to guide students to achieve this excellence.

❖ conveys to students what comprises excellence.

❖ shows students how to evaluate their own work.

❖ shares goals and results.

❖ encourages accurate, unbiased and consistent scoring.

The primary goal of using a rubric for assessment is to improve student learning. When demonstrating rubrics to the class, it is a good idea for teachers to provide examples of each standard. Students and teachers can look at the examples together and use them to guide the student's work.

Evaluating a performance assessment task involves making subjective decisions about the quality of a student's work. A set of scoring guidelines or rubric is a way to make those judgments fairly. A uniform set of defined criteria used to judge student work ensures sound measurement.

SAMPLE RUBRIC DESCRIPTORS

Create your own rubrics with the aid of the following descriptors.
Use the descriptors to qualify expectations of tasks being assessed.

Level 1 Sample Descriptors		
❖ Rarely	❖ Emerging
❖ With constant reminders	❖ Less than half of concepts
❖ Incomplete ways	❖ Direct supervision
❖ Limited understanding	❖ Several errors or omissions

Level 2 Sample Descriptors		
❖ Sometimes	❖ Developing
❖ With some reminders	❖ More than half of concepts
❖ Limited ways	❖ Some supervision
❖ Satisfactory understanding	❖ Some errors or omissions

Level 3 Sample Descriptors		
❖ Usually	❖ Capable
❖ With few reminders	❖ Most concepts
❖ Complete ways	❖ Little supervision
❖ Good understanding	❖ Few errors or omissions

Level 4 Sample Descriptors		
❖ Almost always	❖ Thorough
❖ With almost no reminders	❖ Almost all concepts
❖ Extended ways	❖ No supervision
❖ Excellent understanding	❖ Almost no errors or omission

Assignment details _____

_____

Level 1	

Level 2	

Level 3	

Level 4	

RUBRICS & CHECKLISTS

READING & WRITING

CHECKLIST: PRE-READERS

Student Name _____

	TEACHER COMMENTS
ATTITUDE: ☐ enjoys listening to stories, rhymes or poems ☐ has favorite books	
BOOK KNOWLEDGE: ☐ recognizes the parts of a book ☐ has book handling skills	
ORAL READING: ☐ enjoys playing at reading ☐ enjoys having books reread	
DECODING: ☐ uses pictures to predict text ☐ questions environmental print ☐ recognizes environmental print	
READING COMPREHENSION: ☐ expects print to have meaning ☐ provides a simple retell of familiar text	

CHECKLIST: EMERGENT READERS

Student Name _____

ATTITUDE:	TEACHER COMMENTS
☐ enjoys listening to stories, rhymes and poems ☐ chooses to read as an activity ☐ sees self as a reader	
BOOK KNOWLEDGE: ☐ understands that words being read orally go with the print on the page ☐ knows that illustrations help carry the story ☐ has book handling skills	
ORAL READING: ☐ finger points out words while reading ☐ enjoys reading out loud familiar text	
DECODING: ☐ reads from memory ,but begins to self-correct by observing the print on the page ☐ uses strategies such as picture clues ☐ reads words that repeat in the story	
READING COMPREHENSION: ☐ starts to self-correct using story-line ☐ asks questions about the story ☐ retells a familiar story in sequence	

CHECKLIST: BEGINNING READERS

Student Name _____

	TEACHER COMMENTS
ATTITUDE: ☐ reads to family members ☐ chooses reading as an activity and eager to read longer texts	
BOOK KNOWLEDGE: ☐ has a favourite author	
ORAL READING: ☐ reading is word-by-word or short phrases ☐ reads with little voice intonation	
DECODING: ☐ uses letter sound relationships as a strategy ☐ reads environmental print outside of context ☐ reads on or rereads to regain meaning ☐ uses illustrations to confirm rather to predict text ☐ self- corrects a few words	
READING COMPREHENSION: ☐ starts to show an emotional response to a book ☐ retelling demonstrates some comprehension of plot, character and story sequence	

CHECKLIST: DEVELOPING READERS

Student Name _____

	TEACHER COMMENTS
ATTITUDE: ☐ reads as an independent activity ☐ responds to reading through writing or art	
BOOK KNOWLEDGE: ☐ enjoys matching text to oral language ☐ has a favourite author	
ORAL READING: ☐ reads mostly in short phrases, and some longer phrases ☐ reads according to some punctuation ☐ adjusts some voice intonation to convey meaning ☐ likes to read out loud instead of silently	
DECODING: ☐ begins to self-correct based on meaning ☐ uses parts of words to decode full words ☐ uses patterns and rhymes to help in reading	
READING COMPREHENSION: ☐ retelling demonstrates adequate comprehension of plot, character and story sequence ☐ predicts sequence, plot, character and sequence in the story and makes adjustments	

CHECKLIST: INDEPENDENT READERS

Student Name _____

	TEACHER COMMENTS
ATTITUDE: ☐ becomes engrossed in reading ☐ likes to read silently instead out loud ☐ reads for different purposes ☐ responds to reading through writing or art	
BOOK KNOWLEDGE: ☐ knows there are books for different purposes ☐ uses table of contents, or index to find information ☐ uses a dictionary	
ORAL READING: ☐ usually reads in longer phrases ☐ usually reads according to punctuation ☐ adjusts voice intonation to convey meaning	
DECODING: ☐ derives meaning from context ☐ self-corrects most mistakes ☐ Reads materials that is more difficult	
READING COMPREHENSION: ☐ can brainstorm, classify, predict, confirm and reconstruct stories ☐ skims or scans material to predict content ☐ tells the difference between non-fiction, fiction and fantasy ☐ retelling demonstrates good comprehension of plot, character and story sequence	

READING COMPREHENSION RUBRIC

	Level 1	Level 2	Level 3	Level 4
Prediction	Student is able to anticipate few upcoming events in the text.	Student is able to anticipate some upcoming events in the text.	Student is able to anticipate most upcoming events in the text.	Student is able to anticipate almost all upcoming events in the text.
Personal Response	Student reacts to text content or characters in limited ways or with teacher prompts.	Student reacts to text content or characters in some ways or with some teacher prompts.	Student reacts to text content or characters in developed ways or with few teacher prompts.	Student independently reacts to text content or characters in complete ways.
Self Monitoring	Student keeps reading when comprehension is uncertain, or understanding is minimal.	Student sometimes stops reading when comprehension is uncertain, or understanding is minimal.	Student usually stops reading when comprehension is uncertain, or understanding is minimal.	Student almost always stops reading when comprehension is uncertain, or understanding is minimal.
Story Retell	Student is able to retell and summarize major events during or after reading in limited ways or with teacher prompts.	Student is able to retell and summarize some major events during or after reading.	Student is able to retell and summarize most major events during or after reading.	Student is able to retell and summarize all major events during or after reading.

TEACHER COMMENTS:

_____

_____

_____

_____

_____

_____

_____

CLASS LIST: READING COMPREHENSION

Term _____

Student Name	Prediction	Personal Response	Self Monitoring	Story Retell	Reading Task Focus

ORAL READING RUBRIC

	Level 1	Level 2	Level 3	Level 4
Enjoyment	Student requires prompting and encouragement to read out loud.	Student sometimes requires prompting and encouragement to read out loud.	Student enjoys reading out loud with little prompting to do so.	Student enjoys reading out loud without prompting.
Punctuation	Student struggles to read according to punctuation.	Student sometimes can read according to punctuation.	Student usually reads according to punctuation.	Student consistently reads accurately and according to punctuation.
Expression & Flow	Student rarely reads with expression or flow.	Student sometimes reads with expression and flow.	Student usually reads with expression. Flow is smooth and a good pace.	Student consistently reads with expression. Flow and pace are good.
Decoding Strategies	Student rarely uses strategies to decode text. Teacher prompts required.	Student uses some strategies to decode text. Some teacher prompts required.	Student uses various strategies to decode text. Few teacher prompts required.	Student uses various strategies to decode text, and can explain their use.
Sight vocabulary	Student has limited sight vocabulary.	Student has basic sight vocabulary.	Student has suitable sight vocabulary.	Student has well developed sight vocabulary.

TEACHER COMMENTS:

_____
_____
_____
_____
_____
_____
_____

CLASS LIST: ORAL READING

Term _____

Student Name	Enjoyment	Punctuation	Expression & Flow	Decoding Strategies	Sight Vocabulary

READING CONFERENCE FORM

Date _____   Student's Name _____

What is the title of the book? _____

Who is the author? _____

Have you read other books by this author? _____

_____

Why did you choose this book? _____

_____

DISCUSSION POINTS BASED ON THE STORY READ	TEACHER NOTES/COMMENTS
Does the student comprehend the text? For example: ❖ What was the story about? ❖ Who was the main character(s)? ❖ Where is the setting? ❖ How was the problem solved?	
Does the student make connections between their ideas and the text? For example: ❖ What does …. remind you of?	
Does the student support their opinions with relevant text-based information? ❖ What happened in the story to make you think this?	
What strategies does the student use to decode text? ❖ What kinds of things do you do when you don't know a word?	

WRITTEN RETELL RUBRIC

	Level 1	Level 2	Level 3	Level 4
Story Recall	Student's written retell reveals a partial recall of the story with few events from the story mentioned.	Student's written retell reveals a satisfactory recall of the story sequence with some events from the story mentioned.	Student's written retell reveals a capable recall of the story with most major events from the story mentioned.	Student's written retell reveals an excellent recall of the story with all important events from the story mentioned.
Story Sequence	Student displays little organization in ordering ideas into a beginning, middle and end.	Student displays satisfactory organization in ordering ideas into a beginning, middle and end.	Student displays capable organization in ordering ideas into a beginning, middle and end.	Student competently orders ideas into a beginning, middle and end.
Vocabulary Choice	Student includes few story details or descriptions and limited book language from the story in written retell.	Student includes some details or descriptions and some book language from the story in written retell.	Student includes many details or descriptions and book language from the story in written retell.	Student consistently includes details or descriptions and book language from the story in written retell.
Language Conventions	Student correctly spells few high frequency words. Student displays a limited use of sentence types.	Student correctly spells some high frequency words. Student uses a few sentence types.	Student correctly spells most high frequency words. Student uses a variety of sentence types.	Student correctly spells all high frequency words. Student uses a variety of sentence types is used.

TEACHER COMMENTS:

_____

_____

_____

_____

_____

_____

CLASS LIST: WRITTEN RETELL

Assignment Details _____

_____

Student Name	Story Recall	Story Sequence	Vocabulary Choice	Language Conventions	Overall Mark

WRITTEN RETELL CHECKLIST

Book Title _____

Author _____

Characters

😊 ☹️	I wrote about the main characters in the story.
😊 ☹️	I wrote details about the characters so that others would have a good idea of what they are like.

Setting

😊 ☹️	I wrote about where and when the story takes.
😊 ☹️	I added details to my description of the setting.

Problem

😊 ☹️	I wrote about the problem in the story.

Events

😊 ☹️	I wrote about the important events in the story.
😊 ☹️	I wrote what happened in the beginning, middle and end of the story.

Solution

😊 ☹️	I wrote about how the problem gets solved in the story.

STUDENT WRITING CHECKLIST

My Writing Checklist Name _____

☺ I used a capital letter to start the names of people, places and things.

☺ I used a capital letter to start the beginning of a sentence.

☺ My printing is neat.

☺ I used a period at the end of each sentence.

My Writing Checklist Name _____

☺ I used a capital letter to start the names of people, places and things.

☺ I used a capital letter to start the beginning of a sentence.

☺ My printing is neat.

☺ I used a period at the end of each sentence.

CHECKLIST: BEGINNING WRITERS

Student Name _____

CONTENT AND PURPOSE:

☐ knows that words make the meaning of a story

☐ finds words from environmental print and reading materials

☐ writes one sentence stories for an audience

☐ continues to rehearse a story by drawing a picture

STORY ORDER:

☐ uses simple sentence structure

☐ usually begins sentences the same way

☐ write in directionality of print (left-to-right, top-to-bottom)

EDITING & REVISING:

☐ begins to revise and edit with assistance (adds details, re-reads for omitted letters)

PUNCTUATION & FEATURES OF TEXT:

☐ uses upper and lower case letters

☐ leaves spaces between words

SPELLING:

☐ uses consonants to represent words (initial, final and medial or combinations of all three)

☐ vowels are used simply as place holders

☐ begins to us endings such as s, ed, ing

TEACHER COMMENTS:

_____

_____

_____

_____

_____

CHECKLIST: DEVELOPING WRITERS

Student Name _____

CONTENT AND PURPOSE:

- ☐ includes story titles
- ☐ begins to model writing in style of some authors
- ☐ experiments with styles of writing
- ☐ enjoys writing for an audience

STORY ORDER:

- ☐ uses "run-on" sentence structure ("and then…")
- ☐ tries out a variety of sentence structures
- ☐ writes stories with a beginning, middle and ending

EDITING & REVISING:

- ☐ begins to use a variety of revision techniques such as dictionary, thesaurus, computer word processing tools, etc.

PUNCTUATION & FEATURES OF TEXT:

- ☐ uses upper case letters at the beginning of a sentence, and proper names
- ☐ uses periods, questions marks and exclamation marks

SPELLING:

- ☐ begins to use high frequency words correctly
- ☐ more standardized spelling evident
- ☐ tries to use vowels correctly along with diagraph and blends

TEACHER COMMENTS:

_____

_____

_____

_____

_____

_____

CHECKLIST: INDEPENDENT WRITERS

Student Name _____

CONTENT AND PURPOSE:

- ☐ writes longer stories
- ☐ knows a variety of writing styles (poetic, narrative, opinion, etc.)
- ☐ writes for a specific audience (letter to a friend, email, etc)
- ☐ models story structures from authors read

STORY ORDER:

- ☐ uses complex sentence structure
- ☐ includes dialogue
- ☐ writes logical sequenced stories

EDITING & REVISING:

- ☐ begins to revise and edit independently (adds details, deletes unnecessary details, reorganizes ideas, etc.)

PUNCTUATION & FEATURES OF TEXT:

- ☐ uses correct punctuation
- ☐ begins to write in paragraphs
- ☐ uses punctuation in dialogue

SPELLING:

- ☐ frequently uses standardized spelling
- ☐ understand common spelling patterns
- ☐ approximated spellings are easy to understand and decipher

TEACHER COMMENTS:

_____
_____
_____
_____
_____
_____

CLASS LIST: WRITING PROCESS

Use this class list keep track of what students are working on during each writing class. At the beginning of each writing class, spend a couple of minutes to go down the class list and ask students to state where they are in the writing process. Display a class chart of the writing process for students' easy reference.

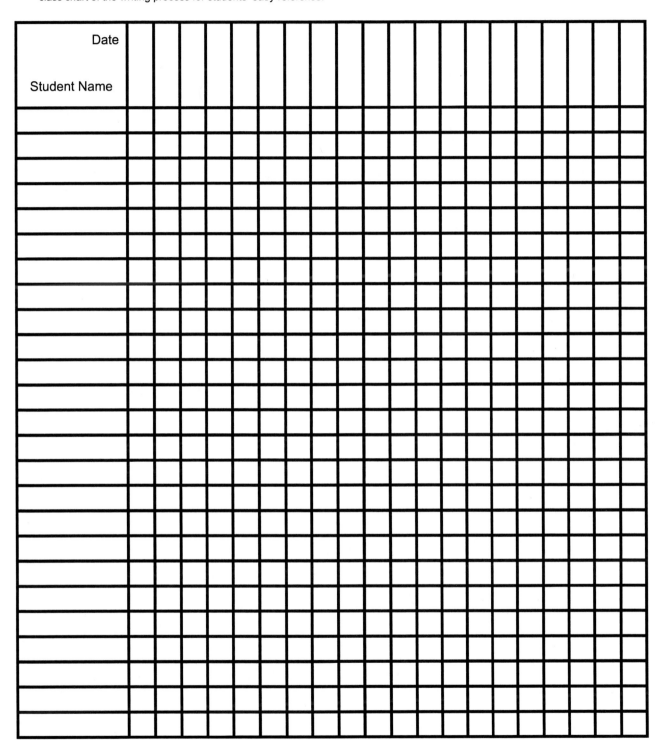

Date Student Name																					

WRITING PROCESS STAGES

S- Story Plan

D- Draft

R- Revision

E- Editing

P- Peer Editing

T- Teacher Conference

G- Good Copy

AC- Ready for the Author Chair

STORY PLANNER

Name _____

Title _____

Write ideas for your story in this story planner.

Where will the adventure take place? (Setting)	Who will be in your adventure? (Characters)

How does the adventure begin?
(Problem)

What happens in your adventure?
(Events)

How does your adventure end?
(Solution)

WRITE A STORY!

Title of story _____

BEGINNING

☐ Who is the story about?

☐ Where does the story take place?

☐ Something interesting.

_____

_____

_____

_____

_____

_____

_____

_____

_____

_____

_____

☐ I checked for capitals and periods.　　　☐ I added detail words.

Story Title _____

MIDDLE

What is the problem in the story?

_____

_____

_____

_____

_____

_____

_____

_____

_____

_____

_____

_____

_____

_____

_____

☐ I checked for capitals and periods.   ☐ I added detail words.

Story Title_____

EVENTS: Write about the things that happen in the story before the problem is solved.

Event 1

_____
_____
_____
_____
_____

Event 2

_____
_____
_____
_____
_____

Event 3

_____
_____
_____
_____
_____

☐ I checked for capitals and periods.

☐ I added detail words.

Story Title_____

ENDING

Write about how the problem is solved.

_____

_____

_____

_____

_____

_____

_____

_____

_____

_____

_____

_____

_____

_____

_____

_____

☐ I checked for capitals and
   periods.

☐ I added detail words.

EDITING MY STORY

Name _____

Title _____

I checked for:

Capitals
- ☐ at the beginning of each sentence
- ☐ in names
- ☐ in dates

Punctuation:
- ☐ . periods at the end of sentences
- ☐ ? question marks at the end of questions
- ☐ ! exclamation marks to show expression

Spelling:
- ☐ in my personal word book
- ☐ in dictionaries
- ☐ in other ways

Sentences with:
- ☐ interesting words
- ☐ missing words

My friend _____ checked for:

Capitals
- ☐ at the beginning of each sentence
- ☐ in names
- ☐ in dates

Punctuation:
- ☐ . periods at the end of sentences
- ☐ ? question marks at the end of questions
- ☐ ! exclamation marks to show expression

Spelling:
- ☐ in my personal word book
- ☐ in dictionaries
- ☐ in other ways

Sentences with:
- ☐ interesting words
- ☐ missing words

REVISING MY STORY

Name _____

Title _____

I checked that my story has:

A beginning that: ☐ introduces the characters.

☐ tells where the story will take place.

A middle that: ☐ tells about a problem or adventure.

☐ tells the reader interesting facts and details.

An ending that: ☐ solves the problem or ends the adventure.

The events are: ☐ in order

☐ clear

☐ interesting

NEXT STEPS

☐ I had a teacher conference. _____

☐ I wrote a good copy of my story.

☐ I drew illustrations to go with my story.

☐ I am ready for the author's chair.

ORAL
COMMUNICATION

&

VISUAL
COMMUNICATION

ORAL PRESENTATION RUBRIC

	Level 1	Level 2	Level 3	Level 4
Preparation	Student is not prepared.	Student is somewhat prepared, but needs more practice.	Student is prepared and has noticeably practiced the presentation.	Student is completely prepared and has noticeably practiced the presentation.
Content Knowledge	Student shows little understanding of the topic.	Student shows a satisfactory understanding of the topic.	Student shows a good understanding of the topic.	Student shows an excellent understanding of the topic.
Assignment Requirements	Assignment requirements are incomplete.	More than half of the assignment requirements are complete.	Assignment requirements are complete.	Assignment requirements are complete and go beyond assignment expectations.
Voice	Student speaks unclearly and uses little voice expression.	Student speaks clearly for some of the time and uses satisfactory voice expression.	Student speaks clearly for most of the time and uses good voice expression.	Student speaks clearly all of the time and uses excellent voice expression.
Eye Contact	Student establishes little or no eye contact with the audience.	Student establishes some eye contact with the audience.	Student establishes good eye contact with the audience.	Student establishes consistent eye contact with the audience.

TEACHER COMMENTS:

_____

_____

_____

_____

_____

CLASS LIST: ORAL PRESENTATION

Assignment Details _____

_____

Student Name	Preparation	Content Knowledge	Assignment Requirements	Voice	Eye Contact	Overall Mark

ORAL PRESENTATION

Name _____

I am going to talk about _____

What I Did	My Presentation
😊 ☹️	I will introduce my topic in an interesting way like with a riddle or a question.
😊 ☹️	I will use my best voice, speak slowly, and make sure it is loud so everyone can hear,
😊 ☹️	I know a lot about my topic.
😊 ☹️	I will write out what I am going to say.
😊 ☹️	I will point to pictures, model, or diorama, as I present.

Think about it!

I am proud of _____

_____

The best part of my presentation was _____

_____

I need to work on _____

I will do better by _____

STORY ORAL RETELL

Name _____

Story Title: _____

Author: _____

	Level 1	Level 2	Level 3	Level 4
I know the story. This means I practiced and didn't need notes to help remember.	☹	😐	🙂	😊
Voice This means I spoke loudly, slowly and clearly.	☹	😐	🙂	😊
Acting This means I used expressive voices, faces and movements. I made the story "real".	☹	😐	🙂	😊
Listening This means I listened to other storytellers.	☹	😐	🙂	😊

Think about it!

I am proud of _____

I need to work on _____

I will do better by _____

POSTER RUBRIC

	Level 1	Level 2	Level 3	Level 4
Poster Appeal	Poor design. Layout is unattractive and messy.	Basic design. Layout and neatness are acceptable.	Interesting design. Layout and neatness are good.	Very well thought out design. Excellent layout and neatness.
Content	Few facts are accurately displayed on the poster.	Some facts are accurately displayed on the poster.	Facts are mostly accurately displayed on the poster.	Facts are accurately displayed on the poster.
Graphic Support	No graphics are related to the topic and no support of the information.	Few graphics are related to the topic and little support of the information.	Most graphics are related to the topic and support the information.	Graphics are related to the topic and support the information.
Assigned Poster Requirements	Several elements were missing. No additional information was added.	Student includes some of the necessary elements but no additional information.	Student includes most of the necessary elements as well as some additional information.	Student includes all necessary elements as well as additional information.

TEACHER COMMENTS:

_____
_____
_____
_____
_____
_____
_____
_____
_____

MAKE A POSTER

Name _____

My poster is about _____

	Level 1	Level 2	Level 3	Level 4
Appearance This means the arrangement of my poster and how it looks.	☹	😐	🙂	😊
Content This means the facts and pictures on my poster.	☹	😐	🙂	😊
Knowledge This means how much I learned from the information on my poster.	☹	😐	🙂	😊
Time This means how I spent the time I was supposed to be working on my poster.	☹	😐	🙂	😊

Think about it!

I am proud of _____

I need to work on _____

I will do better by _____

CLASS LIST: POSTER

Assignment Details _____

_____

Student Name	Poster Appeal	Content	Graphics	Poster Requirements	Overall Mark

HANDWRITING RUBRIC

	Level 1	Level 2	Level 3	Level 4
Letter Formation	Few of the letters are formed correctly.	Some of the letters are formed correctly.	Most of the letters are formed correctly.	All of the letters are formed correctly.
Connection to the Line	Few of the letters are within the lines.	Some of the letters are within the lines.	Most of the letters are within the lines.	All of the letters are within the lines.
Neatness	The letters are difficult to read. Student rushes printing.	Some letters are difficult to read. Student somewhat rushes printing.	Most letters are legible to read. Student takes time to print.	All of the letters are legible to read. Student takes time and care to print.
Application to Daily Work	Printing skills learned are rarely applied to daily work.	Printing skills learned are sometimes applied to daily work.	Printing skills learned are usually applied to daily work.	Printing skills learned are consistently applied to daily work.

TEACHER COMMENTS:

_____

_____

_____

_____

_____

LETTERS THAT THE STUDENT NEEDS TO PRACTICE:

MATHEMATICS

DAILY MATH WORK RUBRIC

	Level 1	Level 2	Level 3	Level 4
Understanding of Math Concepts	Student demonstrates a limited understanding of math concepts in daily work.	Student demonstrates a satisfactory understanding of taught in daily work.	Student demonstrates a complete understanding of math concepts in daily work.	Student demonstrates a thorough understanding of math concepts in daily work.
Application of Skills Taught	Student rarely applies skills taught in daily work without teacher assistance.	Student applies skills taught in daily work with several errors and omissions.	Student applies skills taught in daily work with few errors and omissions.	Student consistently applies skills taught in daily work with almost no errors and omissions.
Math Terminology	Student rarely uses appropriate math terms during math discussions and activities.	Student sometimes uses appropriate math terms during math discussions and activities.	Student usually uses appropriate math terms during math discussions and activities.	Student consistently uses appropriate math terms during math discussions and activities.
Attendance to Task	Student rarely stays on task.	Student sometimes stays on task.	Student usually stays on task.	Student always stays on task.

TEACHER COMMENTS:

_____

_____

_____

_____

_____

_____

_____

_____

MATH WORK CHECKLIST

I did the following: Name: _____

- ☐ I drew pictures or diagrams to help me solve the problem.
- ☐ I showed all the steps in solving the problem.
- ☐ I named the operations I used to solve the problem.
- ☐ I used math language to explain my thinking.

....

MATH WORK CHECKLIST

I did the following: Name: _____

- ☐ I drew pictures or diagrams to help me solve the problem.
- ☐ I showed all the steps in solving the problem.
- ☐ I named the operations I used to solve the problem.
- ☐ I used math language to explain my thinking.

....

MATH WORK CHECKLIST

I did the following: Name: _____

- ☐ I drew pictures or diagrams to help me solve the problem.
- ☐ I showed all the steps in solving the problem.
- ☐ I named the operations I used to solve the problem.
- ☐ I used math language to explain my thinking.

QUALITY MATH NOTE BOOK CHECKLIST

Name _____

☐ There is a title and date on each page.

☐ Work is complete and neatly organized.

☐ Calculations are labeled and done in pencil.

☐ Questions are copied and the solutions are underneath.

....

QUALITY MATH NOTE BOOK CHECKLIST

Name _____

☐ There is a title and date on each page.

☐ Work is complete and neatly organized.

☐ Calculations are labeled and done in pencil.

☐ Questions are copied and the solutions are underneath.

....

QUALITY MATH NOTE BOOK CHECKLIST

Name _____

☐ There is a title and date on each page.

☐ Work is complete and neatly organized.

☐ Calculations are labeled and done in pencil.

☐ Questions are copied and the solutions are underneath.

PROBLEM SOLVING CHECKLIST

Name _____

☐ I carefully read the problem.

☐ I listed known numbers, and important information.

☐ I drew a labeled diagram to help solve the problem.

☐ I showed my work for every step in solving the problem.

☐ I stated the solution, and showed the units.

☐ I used math language to explain my thinking.

☐ I printed neatly, and spaced out my work.

☐ I checked my calculations over.

....

PROBLEM SOLVING CHECKLIST

Name _____

☐ I carefully read the problem.

☐ I listed known numbers, and important information.

☐ I drew a labeled diagram to help solve the problem.

☐ I showed my work for every step in solving the problem.

☐ I stated the solution, and showed the units.

☐ I used math language to explain my thinking.

☐ I printed neatly, and spaced out my work.

☐ I checked my calculations over.

GRADE 1 NUMBER CONCEPTS

Student Name _____ Date _____

Expectation	Level 1 Not Yet	Level 2 Developing	Level 3 Proficient	Level 4 Mastered
counts orally by 1's, 2's, 5's and 10's to 100				
reads number words to 10				
understands numerals, ordinals, and the corresponding words, and demonstrate the ability to print them				
understands the concept of order by sequencing events				
compares and orders whole numbers using concrete materials and drawings to develop number meanings				
represents fractions (halves as part of a whole) using concrete materials				
understands and explains basic operations addition of whole numbers by modeling				
understands and explains basic operations subtraction of whole numbers by modeling				
develops proficiency in adding one-digit whole numbers				
solves simple problems involving counting, joining, and taking one group away from another and describes and explains the strategies used				
estimates quantity in everyday life (e.g., guess, then count how many buttons are in the glass)				
uses a calculator to explore counting and to solve problems beyond the required pencil-and-paper skills.				

Level 1 Student rarely applies skills with several errors or omissions.
Level 2 Student sometimes applies skills with some errors or omissions.
Level 3 Student usually applies skills with few errors or omissions.
Level 4 Student consistently applies skills with almost no errors or omissions.

GRADE 2 NUMBER CONCEPTS

Student Name _____ Date _____

Expectation	Level 1 Not Yet	Level 2 Developing	Level 3 Proficient	Level 4 Mastered
reads and prints number words to twenty				
counts by 1's, 2's, 5's, 10's, and 25's beyond 100 using multiples of 1, 2, and 5 as starting points				
counts backwards by 1's from 20				
locates whole numbers to 50 on a number line and partial number line				
shows counting by 2's, 5's, and 10's to 50 on a number line				
compares, orders, and represents whole numbers to 100 using concrete materials and drawings				
uses ordinal numbers to thirty-first				
represents multiplication as repeated addition using concrete materials				
demonstrates division as sharing				
recalls addition facts to 18				
recalls subtraction facts to 18				
represents and explains halves, thirds, and quarters as part of a whole and part of a set using concrete materials and drawings				
adds two-digit numbers with and without regrouping, with sums less than 101, using concrete materials				
subtracts two-digit numbers with and without regrouping, with sums less than 101, using concrete materials				
adds and subtracts money amounts to 100¢ using concrete materials, drawings & symbols				

Level 1 Student rarely applies skills with several errors or omissions.
Level 2 Student sometimes applies skills with some errors or omissions.
Level 3 Student usually applies skills with few errors or omissions.
Level 4 Student consistently applies skills with almost no errors or omissions.

GRADE 3 NUMBER CONCEPTS

Student Name _____ Date _____

Expectation	Level 1 Not Yet	Level 2 Developing	Level 3 Proficient	Level 4 Mastered
reads and prints numerals from 0 to 1000				
reads and prints number words to one hundred				
counts by 1's, 2's, 5's, 10's, and 100's to 1000 using various starting points and by 25's to 1000 using multiples of 25 as starting points				
counts backwards by 2's, 5's, and 10's from 100 using multiples of 2, 5, and 10 as starting points and by 100's from any number less than 1001				
uses ordinal numbers to hundredth				
demonstrates, concretely and pictorially, place value concepts to give meaning to numbers up to 1000				
represents and explains common fractions, presented in real-life situations, as part of a whole, part of a set, and part of a measure using concrete materials and drawings				
recalls addition and subtraction facts to 18				
determines the value of the missing term in an addition sent				
demonstrates and recalls multiplication facts to 7 x 7 using concrete materials				
demonstrates and recalls division facts to 49 ÷ 7 using concrete materials				
identifies numbers that are divisible by 2, 5, or 10				
mentally adds and subtracts one-digit and two-digit numbers				
adds and subtracts three-digit numbers with and without regrouping using concrete materials				
adds and subtracts money amounts and represents the answer in decimal notation				

Level 1 Student rarely applies skills with several errors or omissions.
Level 2 Student sometimes applies skills with some errors or omissions.
Level 3 Student usually applies skills with few errors or omissions.
Level 4 Student consistently applies skills with almost no errors or omissions.

VISUAL ARTS

DANCE/ MOVEMENT

DRAMA

GENERAL VISUAL ARTS RUBRIC

	Level 1	Level 2	Level 3	Level 4
Art Appreciation	Student expresses opinions about art in limited ways. Teacher prompts are needed.	Student sometimes expresses opinions about art with some teacher prompts.	Student usually expresses opinions about art with few teacher prompts.	Student consistently expresses opinions about art.
Critical Analysis	Student does not use evidence from artwork to support their interpretation.	Student supports their interpretation using little evidence from the art work.	Student supports their interpretation using satisfactory evidence from the art work.	Student supports their interpretation using extensive evidence from the art work.
Creative Work	Student applies less than half of the skills, techniques and concepts taught.	Student applies over half of the skills techniques and concepts taught.	Student applies most of the skills techniques and concepts taught.	Student applies almost all of the skills techniques and concepts taught.
Use of Tools and Materials	Student needs constant reminders to use tools and materials appropriately.	Student needs some reminders to use tools and materials appropriately.	Student needs little reminders to use tools and materials appropriately.	Student rarely needs reminders to use tools and materials appropriately.
Communication	Student rarely uses correct terminology.	Student sometimes uses correct terminology.	Student usually uses correct terminology.	Student consistently uses correct terminology.

TEACHER COMMENTS:

_____
_____
_____
_____
_____
_____

CLASS LIST: GENERAL VISUAL ARTS

Student Name	Art Appreciation	Critical Analysis	Creative Work	Use of Tools	Communication

TEACHER CHECKLIST: VISUAL ARTS

o Encourage students to do their own artwork.

o Exhibit students' artwork.

o Encourage students to be inventive.

o Encourage students to finish their artwork.

o Encourage students to talk about their artwork .

o Provide ample time and opportunity to do art.

o Teach and model how to care for materials.

o Encourage students to experiment with various media.

o Encourage students to be observant and aware of their environment.

o Be enthusiastic and have fun!

DANCE/MOVEMENT RUBRIC

	Level 1	Level 2	Level 3	Level 4
Understanding of Concepts	Student rarely performs all steps correctly.	Student sometimes performs all steps correctly.	Student usually performs all steps correctly.	Student consistently performs all steps correctly.
Application of Skills	Student applies skills learned in limited ways to own creative works.	Student applies skills learned in some ways to own creative works.	Student applies skills learned in complete ways to own creative works.	Student applies skills learned in extended ways to own creative works.
Rhythm	Student rarely stays in rhythm and holds head up and faces forward.	Student sometimes stays in rhythm and holds head up and faces forward.	Student usually stays in rhythm and holds head up and faces forward.	Student consistently stays in rhythm and holds head up and faces forward.
Participation	Student rarely shows enthusiasm and energy during activities.	Student sometimes shows enthusiasm and energy during activities.	Student usually shows enthusiasm and energy during activities.	Student consistently shows enthusiasm and energy during activities.
Communication of Concepts	Student rarely uses correct terminology when describing or interpreting their own and others' work.	Student sometimes uses correct terminology when describing or interpreting their own and others' work.	Student usually uses correct terminology when describing or interpreting their own and others' work.	Student consistently uses correct terminology when describing or interpreting their own and others' work.

TEACHER COMMENTS:

_____

_____

_____

_____

_____

_____

_____

CLASS LIST: DANCE/MOVEMENT

Student Name	Understanding of Concepts	Application of Skills	Rhythm	Participation	Communication of Concepts

DRAMA RUBRIC

	Level 1	Level 2	Level 3	Level 4
Understanding of Concepts	Student demonstrates a limited understanding of voice and audience by speaking and writing in role as characters in a story.	Student demonstrates a satisfactory understanding of voice and audience by speaking and writing in role as characters in a story.	Student demonstrates a good understanding of voice and audience by speaking and writing in role as characters in a story.	Student demonstrates a thorough understanding of voice and audience by speaking and writing in role as characters in a story.
Application of Skills	Student applies skills learned in limited ways to own creative works.	Student applies skills learned in some ways to own creative works.	Student applies skills learned in complete ways to own creative works.	Student applies skills learned in extended ways to own creative works.
Voice	Student rarely varies intonation or expression.	Student sometimes intonation or	Student usually intonation or holds head up and faces forward.	Student consistently intonation or holds head up and faces forward.
Performance	Student performs with limited feeling and expression and fails to engage the audience.	Student performs with some feeling and expression and has a limited engagement of the audience.	Student performs with feeling and expression and engages the audience.	Student performs with impressive feeling and expression and has completely engages the audience.
Participation	Student rarely shows enthusiasm and energy during activities.	Student sometimes shows enthusiasm and energy during activities.	Student usually shows enthusiasm and energy during activities.	Student consistently shows enthusiasm and energy during activities.
Communication of Concepts	Student rarely uses correct terminology when describing or interpreting their own and others' work.	Student sometimes uses correct terminology when describing or interpreting their own and others' work.	Student usually uses correct terminology when describing or interpreting their own and others' work.	Student consistently uses correct terminology when describing or interpreting their own and others' work.

CLASS LIST: DRAMA

Student Name	Understanding of Concepts	Application of Skills	Voice	Participation	Communication of Concepts

SCIENCE
&
SOCIAL
STUDIES

GENERAL SCIENCE RUBRIC

	Level 1	Level 2	Level 3	Level 4
Comprehension of Science Concepts	Student displays a limited understanding of concepts and how they relate to daily life.	Student displays a satisfactory understanding of concepts and how they relate to daily life.	Student displays a good understanding of concepts and how they relate to daily life.	Student displays a thorough understanding of concepts and how they relate to daily life.
Procedure Skills	Student applies few of the required skills and needs teacher support.	Student applies some of the required skills and needs some teacher support.	Student applies most of the required skills and needs infrequent teacher support.	Student applies almost all of the required skills and needs no teacher support.
Safety	Student uses tools, equipment, and materials correctly only with teacher supervision.	Student uses tools, equipment, and materials correctly with some teacher supervision.	Student uses tools, equipment, and materials correctly with little teacher supervision.	Student uses tools, equipment, and materials correctly without teacher supervision.
Communication Skills	Student rarely uses correct science terminology when discussing science concepts.	Student sometimes uses correct science terminology when discussing science concepts.	Student usually uses correct science terminology when discussing science concepts.	Student consistently uses correct science terminology when discussing science concepts.

TEACHER COMMENTS:

_____
_____
_____
_____
_____
_____
_____

CLASS LIST: GENERAL SCIENCE

SCIENCE FOCUS: _____

Student Name	Comprehension of Science Concepts	Procedure Skills	Safety	Communication	Overall Mark

SCIENCE SAFETY CHECKLIST

➢ Follow the teacher's directions.

➢ Keep your hands to yourself.

➢ Keep your hands clean.

➢ Keep your equipment clean.

➢ Put things back.

➢ Do not eat or smell anything.

Be safe with tools, equipment and materials!

SCIENCE EXPERIMENT RUBRIC

	Level 1	Level 2	Level 3	Level 4
Understanding of Concept	Student displays a limited understanding of the experiment concept and how it works.	Student displays a satisfactory understanding of the experiment concept and how it works.	Student displays a good understanding of the experiment concept and how it works.	Student displays a thorough understanding of the experiment concept and how it works.
Experiment Design	Student applies few of the required skills and strategies to carry out the experiment successfully. The experiment is incomplete.	Student applies some of the required skills and strategies to carry out the experiment successfully. The experiment is complete.	Student applies most of the required skills and strategies to carry out the experiment successfully. The experiment is complete.	Student applies almost all of required skills and strategies to carry out the experiment successfully. The experiment is complete.
Concepts and Skills Connections	Student shows little understanding of how the experiment connects to a real world application within a familiar context.	Student shows some understanding of how the experiment connects to a real world application within a familiar context.	Student shows good understanding of how the experiment connects to a real world application within a familiar context.	Student shows complete understanding of how the experiment connects to a real world application within a familiar context.
Safety	Student uses tools, equipment, and materials correctly only with teacher supervision.	Student uses tools, equipment, and materials correctly with some teacher supervision.	Student uses tools, equipment, and materials correctly with little teacher supervision.	Student uses tools, equipment, and materials correctly without teacher supervision.
Communication Skills	Student rarely uses correct science terminology introduced in the experiment.	Student sometimes uses correct science terminology introduced in the experiment.	Student usually uses correct science terminology introduced in the experiment.	Student consistently uses correct science terminology introduced in the experiment.

TEACHER COMMENTS:

_____

_____

_____

CLASS LIST: SCIENCE EXPERIMENT

Experiment: _____

Student Name	Understanding of Concept	Experiment Design	Concept and Skills Connections	Safety	Communication	Overall Mark

GENERAL SOCIAL STUDIES RUBRIC

	Level 1	Level 2	Level 3	Level 4
Comprehension of Social Studies Concepts	Student displays a limited understanding of concepts.	Student displays a satisfactory understanding of concepts.	Student displays a good understanding of concepts.	Student displays a thorough understanding of concepts.
Mapping Skills	Student applies few of the required mapping skills and needs teacher support.	Student applies some of the mapping required skills and needs some teacher support.	Student applies most of the mapping required skills and needs infrequent teacher support.	Student applies almost all of the required mapping skills and needs no teacher support.
Social Studies Concepts and Skills Connections	Student relates concepts to personal experience or prior knowledge or the outside world in limited ways.	Student relates some concepts to personal experience or prior knowledge or the outside world.	Student relates most concepts to personal experience or prior knowledge or the outside world.	Student relates almost all concepts to personal experience or prior knowledge or the outside world.
Communication Skills	Student rarely uses correct social studies terminology and symbols.	Student sometimes uses correct social studies terminology and symbols	Student usually uses correct social studies terminology and symbols	Student consistently uses correct social studies terminology and symbols

TEACHER COMMENTS:

_____

_____

_____

_____

_____

_____

_____

CLASS LIST: GENERAL SOCIAL STUDIES

Social Studies Focus _____

Student Name	Comprehension of Concepts	Mapping Skills	Social Studies Connections	Communication Skills	Overall Mark

CANADA'S TRADITIONS & CELEBRATIONS RUBRIC

	Level 1	Level 2	Level 3	Level 4
Demonstrates an understanding that Canada is a country of many cultures	Student provides limited examples to show Canada may be made up of many cultures.	Student provides examples with some details to show Canada may be made up of many cultures.	Student provides considerable examples with many details to show Canada may be made up of many cultures.	Student provides comprehensive examples with extensive details to show Canada may be made up of many cultures.
Identifies community celebrations that reflect their heritage and Canadian identity	Student can identify few features of celebrations with limited detail. Provides basic information.	Student can identify features of celebrations with some detail. Provides clear information.	Student can identify many features of celebrations with considerable detail. Provides supporting information and is able to answer questions.	Student can identify comprehensive features of celebrations with high degree of detail. Provides supporting information and is able to answer questions with extensive explanations.
Describes family history and traditions made by individuals and groups in the local community	Student communicates about traditions and celebrations with limited understanding and few details.	Student communicates about traditions and celebrations with understanding and details.	Student communicates about traditions and celebrations with demonstrated understanding and good details.	Student communicates about traditions and celebrations with detailed understanding and accurate explanations.

TEACHER COMMENTS:

_____

_____

_____

_____

_____

PHYSICAL EDUCATION

PHYSICAL EDUCATION RUBRIC

	Level 1	Level 2	Level 3	Level 4
Understanding of Physical Education Concepts	Student demonstrates a limited understanding of concepts.	Student demonstrates a satisfactory understanding of concepts.	Student demonstrates a complete understanding of concepts.	Student demonstrates a thorough understanding of concepts.
Application of Skills Taught	Student applies few of the required skills.	Student applies some of the required skills.	Student applies most of the required skills.	Student applies almost all of the required skills.
Participation	Student rarely participates actively. Constant teacher encouragement is needed.	Student sometimes participates actively. Some teacher encouragement is needed.	Student usually participates actively. Little teacher encouragement is needed.	Student almost always participates actively without teacher encouragement
Sportsmanship	Student behavior interferes with own learning. Student needs encouragement to be a team player.	Student behavior occasionally interferes with own learning. Student will sometimes share, help and encourage others.	Student behavior rarely interferes with own learning. Student will usually share, help and encourage others.	Student acts as a team leader. Student will consistently share, help, and encourage others.
Safety	Student requires constant reminders regarding safety or the safe use of equipment and facilities.	Student requires some reminders regarding safety or the safe use of equipment and facilities.	Student requires few reminders regarding safety or the safe use of equipment and facilities.	Student requires almost no reminders regarding safety or the safe use of equipment and facilities.

TEACHER COMMENTS:

_____

_____

_____

CLASS LIST: PHYSICAL EDUCATION

Physical Education Focus: _____

Student Name	Understanding Concepts	Application of Skills	Participation	Sportsmanship	Safety	Overall Mark

LEARNING SKILLS

LEARNING SKILLS RUBRIC

	Level 1	Level 2	Level 3	Level 4
Attendance	Student is late more than twice a week and/or attends class infrequently.	Student is occasionally late and/or attends class most of the time.	Student is rarely late and/or attends class regularly.	Student is always prompt and/or attends class regularly.
Behavior	Student needs constant teacher reminders about appropriate behavior.	Student sometimes needs teacher reminders about appropriate behavior.	Student rarely needs teacher reminders about appropriate behavior.	Student almost never needs teacher reminders about appropriate behavior.
Class Preparation	Student is rarely prepared and organized for class.	Student is sometimes prepared and organized for class.	Student is usually prepared and organized for class.	Student is almost always prepared and organized for class.
Listening Skills	Student rarely listens to others and speaks out of turn. Constant teacher reminders are needed.	Student sometimes listens to others and sometimes speaks out of turn. Some teacher reminders are needed.	Student usually listens to others and rarely speaks out of turn. Few teacher reminders are needed.	Student almost always listens to others and almost never speaks out of turn.
Time Management	Student rarely finishes work in the allotted time.	Student sometimes finishes work in the allotted time.	Student usually finishes work in the allotted time.	Student almost always finishes work in the allotted time.
Learning Attitude	Student rarely displays a positive attitude towards learning.	Student sometimes displays a positive attitude towards learning.	Student usually displays a positive attitude towards learning.	Student consistently displays a positive attitude towards learning.

CLASS LIST: LEARNING SKILLS

Time Period_____

Student Name	Attendance	Behaviour	Class Preparation	Listening Skills	Time Management	Learning Attitude

CLASS LIST: STUDENT PARTICIPATION

Subject _____

Date / Student Name																							

Level 1 Student rarely contributes to class discussions and activities by offering ideas and asking questions.

Level 2 Student sometimes contributes to class discussions and activities by offering ideas and asking questions.

Level 3 Student usually contributes to class discussions and activities by offering ideas and asking questions.

Level 4 Student consistently contributes to class discussions and activities by offering ideas and asking questions.

LEARNING SKILLS   Name _____

I use class time wisely.	☹	😐	🙂
My materials are organized.	☹	😐	🙂
I have good work habits.	☹	😐	🙂
I am a good group member.	☹	😐	🙂
I follow directions.	☹	😐	🙂

Think about it!

I am proud of _____

_____

I need to work on _____

_____

I will do better by _____

_____

LEARNING SKILLS

Name _____

	Level 1	Level 2	Level 3	Level 4
Use of Time	I need lots of help from friends or the teacher	I needed some help from friends or the teacher	I didn't need lots of help from friends or the teacher	I was able to work without help from friends or the teacher.
Organization	My work is not always complete. I need to plan ahead.	My work is sometimes complete. I need to plan ahead.	My work is usually complete. I usually plan ahead.	My work is always complete. I plan ahead.
Work Habits	I have trouble keeping things neat. I do not always stay on task.	I sometimes keep things neat. I sometimes stay on task.	I almost always keep things neat. I usually stay on task.	I always keep things neat. I almost always stay on task.
Group Work	I have trouble working in a group.	I sometimes work well in a group.	I work well in a group. Sometimes I take the leadership role.	I always work well in a group. I usually take the leadership role.
Following Directions	I need reminders to follow directions.	I sometimes follow directions.	I usually follow directions.	I follow directions.

Think about it!

I am proud of _____

_____

I need to work on _____

I will do better by _____

CLASS LIST: HOMEWORK COMPLETION

Subject _____

Student Name / Date																						

Level 1 Less than the half of the required homework is complete.

Level 2 More than half of the required homework is complete.

Level 3 Homework is complete.

Level 4 Homework is complete and has added detail.

SELF- EVALUATION

Name _____

The best part was……

_____

_____

_____

I learned about……..

_____

_____

_____

I want to learn more about….

_____

_____

_____

My Work Habits

	Almost Always	Sometimes	I need to try harder.
I listened to the teacher.			
I tried my best to work on my own.			
I did neat work with lots of details.			
I was a good group member.			
I did my work on time and with care.			

STUDENT SELF-ASSESSMENT RUBRIC

WOW	✓ I completed my work independently on time and with care. ✓ I added details and followed the instructions without help. ✓ I understand and can talk about what I have learned.
BRAVO	✓ I completed my work on time and with care. ✓ I followed the instructions with almost no help. ✓ I understand and can talk about what I have learned.
OKAY	✓ I completed my work. ✓ I followed the instructions with some help. ✓ I understand and can talk about most of what I have learned.
UH-OH	✓ I need to complete my work on time and with care. ✓ I should ask for help when I need it. ✓ I understand and can talk about a few of the things that I have learned.

Post the above rubric in your classroom to assist children in self- evaluation and direction for improvement in completing the tasks assigned.

MATH FOCUS _____

Student Name _____

Expectation	Level 1 Not Yet	Level 2 Developing	Level 3 Proficient	Level 4 Mastered

Level 1 Student rarely applies skills with several errors or omissions.
Level 2 Student sometimes applies skills with some errors or omissions.
Level 3 Student usually applies skills with few errors or omissions.
Level 4 Student consistently applies skills with almost no errors or omissions.

GeoWat Innovative Teacher Publishing © 2005

STUDENT RUBRIC

Name _____

This a rubric about _____

What I Did	Expectation
😊 ☹️	
😊 ☹️	
😊 ☹️	
😊 ☹️	
😊 ☹️	

Think about it!

I am proud of _____

_____

The best part was _____

_____

I need to work on _____

I will do better by _____

A QUICK RUBRIC

Use these face rubrics as a quick way to evaluate work.

GREAT EFFORT!

Congratulations to

_____

 BRAVO!

Keep up the effort!

_____

Quality Worker

★ ★ ★ ★ ★ ★